GCSE AQA English
Understanding Non-Fiction Texts
The Workbook

This book is for anyone doing **GCSE AQA English** or
GCSE AQA English Language at foundation level.

It contains lots of **tricky questions** designed to hone your **reading skills**
— because that's the only way you'll get any **better**.

It's also got some daft bits in to try and make the whole
experience at least vaguely entertaining for you.

What CGP is all about

Our sole aim here at CGP is to produce the highest quality
books — carefully written, immaculately presented and
dangerously close to being funny.

Then we work our socks off to get them out to you
— at the cheapest possible prices.

CONTENTS

Section Five — Exam Techniques

Section Six — Sample Exam

Section Seven — Practice Exam

Published by Coordination Group Publications Ltd.

Editors:
Joe Brazier
Charley Darbishire
Kate Houghton
Katherine Reed
Edward Robinson
Caley Simpson
Jennifer Underwood

Contributors:
Jane Harrison

ISBN: 978 1 84146 887 7

With thanks to Heather Gregson, Barbara Brecht and Jeffrey Emmett for the proofreading.
With thanks to Laura Stoney for the copyright research.

Groovy website: www.cgpbooks.co.uk
Jolly bits of clipart from CorelDRAW®
Printed by Elanders Hindson Ltd, Newcastle upon Tyne.

Based on the classic CGP style created by Richard Parsons.

The Audience

Q1 For each sentence, circle the word which best describes the audience it is aimed at. The first one has been done for you.

a) "Do you long for a simpler, more reliable way of managing your finances?"

children / (adults)

b) "When you play netball, first of all you have to decide which position you would like to play."

experts / beginners

c) "No trip to China is complete without seeing the famous and fabulous Great Wall."

tourists / business people

Q2 What sort of people would you expect to read these publications?

a) *The Rough Guide to Turkey*   ....

b) *The Times Educational Supplement*   ....

c) *The Big Book of Car Games*   ....

Q3 Read the text below and answer the question underneath.   MINI-ESSAY QUESTION

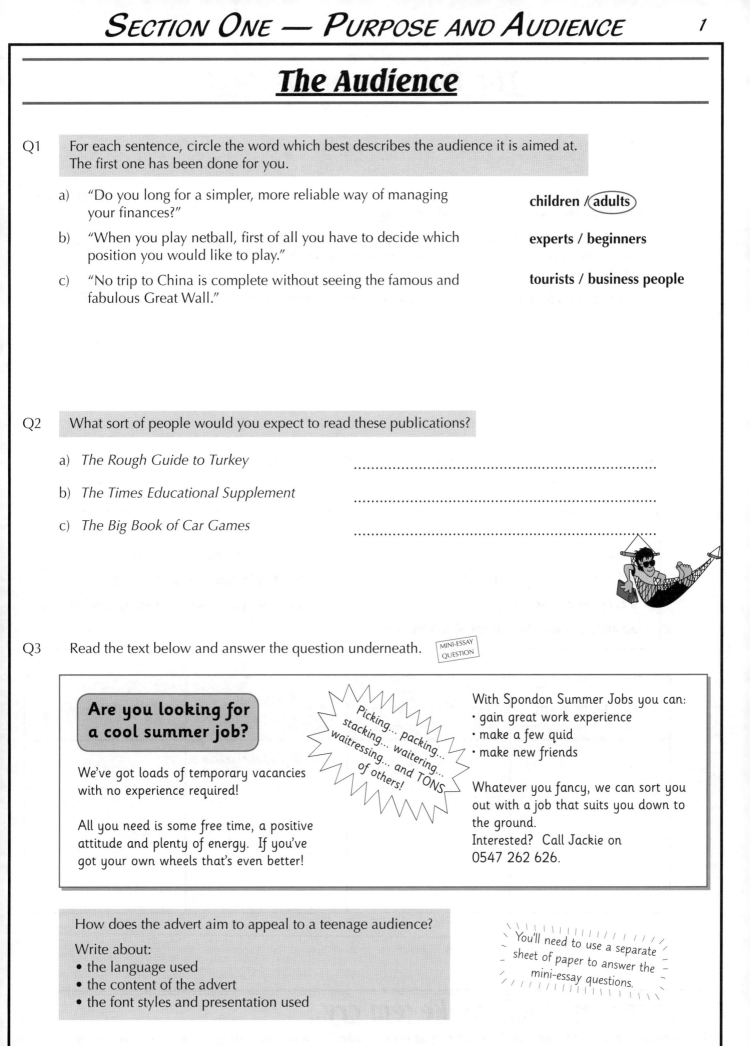

Are you looking for a cool summer job?

We've got loads of temporary vacancies with no experience required!

All you need is some free time, a positive attitude and plenty of energy. If you've got your own wheels that's even better!

Picking... packing... stacking... waiting... waitressing... waitering... and TONS of others!

With Spondon Summer Jobs you can:
· gain great work experience
· make a few quid
· make new friends

Whatever you fancy, we can sort you out with a job that suits you down to the ground.
Interested? Call Jackie on
0547 262 626.

How does the advert aim to appeal to a teenage audience?
Write about:
• the language used
• the content of the advert
• the font styles and presentation used

You'll need to use a separate sheet of paper to answer the mini-essay questions.

The Purpose of the Text

Q1   Draw lines to match each type of text to its main purpose.

a)   "Who could disagree with the fact that children should eat healthily?
Child obesity is on the rise — and we need to stop it."   **To entertain**

b)   "As the train moved south, first crawling, then increasing to a steady gallop,
the scenery gradually changed from the flat and drab to the dramatic and
beautiful."   **To inform**

c)   "Shop around for the best quote — some insurers are much more expensive
than others."   **To persuade**

d)   "Tomorrow, there will be scattered showers in the north-west."   **To advise**

Q2   Put each of the following types of text in the correct column in the table, based on its main purpose.
The first one has been done for you. You may find that some of these fit into more than one column.

a charity advertisement   **a film review**

a cake recipe   **an agony aunt column in a magazine**

a leaflet from a political party   **an instruction manual for a computer**

a cartoon in a newspaper   **a leaflet with tips on how to give up smoking**

an article about the Industrial Revolution

Texts that inform	Texts that entertain	Texts that argue or persuade	Texts that advise
		a charity advertisement	

Make 'em laugh, make 'em cry...

Authors don't just write the first thing that comes into their heads. They've usually got a purpose
in mind — and they try and write in a way which helps them achieve it.

Informative and Entertaining Texts

Q1   Put an **I** next to the statement that is informative, and an **E** next to the one that is entertaining.

   a)   "Steven Morrissey was born in Manchester on 22nd May 1959."

   b)   "The gig was absolute mayhem. Swathes of bodies ebbed and flowed in a sea of craziness — enjoyment and a survival instinct competed for my attention."

Is that all I'm here for — your entertainment?

Q2   Pick out two words or phrases that are entertaining and two words or phrases that are informative from the text below.

> Thai food can be startlingly hot, so watch out! The chefs around here get through chillies like you wouldn't believe — though some relief comes from the creamy coconut milk that tames the fire of the burning hot curries. If you visit Bangkok, there's a very well-respected restaurant you can visit called the 'Koh San Garden'. It has an extensive menu, with more than fifty freshly-made dishes to choose from.

Informative words or phrases:

1)   ....

2)   ....

Entertaining words or phrases:

1)   ....

2)   ....

Q3   Read the two texts below, then decide which text is more informative and which text is more entertaining. Write a brief explanation for each of your answers.

   a)   The Battle of Hastings was fought on October 14th 1066 on a field near Hastings in East Sussex. William the Conqueror led the invading Normans in their most important victory over the Anglo-Saxons and their King, Harold II.

This text is **entertaining / informative** because ....

....

   b)   The battle was furious and bloody, with vast numbers of soldiers being brutally murdered. At one stage the English were fooled into thinking they had won the battle, and stormed towards their enemy, only to find themselves ambushed and mercilessly beaten.

This text is **entertaining / informative** because ....

....

Texts that Argue, Persuade or Advise

Q1 Draw lines to match each statement below to its purpose.

    a) "If you want to make a difference, there are many organisations you can join."

                                      to persuade

    b) "By joining our march and signing this petition, you will be helping to put an end to this disgraceful act of cruelty."

                                        to advise

Q2 For each text, circle whether you think its purpose is to argue, to persuade or to advise, and briefly explain your answer.

    a)

> The bad language used by youngsters today is disgraceful. What's more, they seem to have no respect for authority. Society is a worse place as a result.

I think the purpose is to **argue / persuade / advise** because ....

....

    b)

> A stern telling-off after bad behaviour is often all that is needed to ensure your child grows into a responsible, considerate individual.

I think the purpose is to **argue / persuade / advise** because ....

....

Q3 Read the extract from a leaflet below and then answer the question about it underneath. MINI-ESSAY QUESTION

> **Come to Rufford Aquarium — you'll have a whale of a time!**
>
> Rufford Aquarium is the only place in the county where you can see local and exotic species of fish and sea mammals all in one place.
>
> Experience the magic of the deep as you are surrounded by the underwater world. You could be eyed up by an octopus, shaken by a shark or peered at by pike!
>
> Whatever your age, you're guaranteed a fantastic time.
>
> *Entry costs:* Adult — £6   Child — £3   Family ticket — £15
>
> **Rufford Aquarium — a great family day out!**

How does the presentation and choice of language persuade the reader to visit the aquarium? Write about:
- font size and style
- language techniques (e.g. rule of three, alliteration, puns)

Formal Style and Informal Style

Q1   For each pair of sentences, underline the more formal sentence.

a)   "Sorry! We don't take credit cards."
     "Customers are advised that we do not accept credit cards."

b)   "It is essential to ensure you have the correct tools before proceeding."
     "Check you've got the proper kit to hand before you go any further."

Sorry Sir, we don't accept credit cards — you're going to have to go in the kitchen and wash up.

Q2   Put each language feature in the correct column, based on where you would usually expect to find it.

non-standard English

standard English

complex sentences

simple sentences

light-hearted tone

serious tone

contractions (e.g. "don't")

impersonal style

personal style

humour

Formal texts	Informal texts

Q3   The text below is taken from a travel journal. Is the style of the text formal or informal?
Write down two pieces of evidence from the text that back up your answer.

> At this point on my train journey I was starting to get a tad — how shall I put it? — narked off.
> It's one thing being patient, accepting the fact that things don't always go to plan and that now
> and then delays just happen. It's quite another to be told, after paying good money for a ticket
> on the grounds that it's taking you to Town A, that apparently for no good reason we're taking a
> little detour through Village B, River C and Swamp D.

The style is **informal / formal** because:

1) ....

2) ....

I like your style...

The style a writer chooses has to be right for the audience. If you can work out who the audience
is, it will help you understand <u>why</u> the writer has chosen to write in a particular <u>style</u>.

Personal Tone and Impersonal Tone

Q1   Write a **P** for "personal" or an **I** for "impersonal" to describe the
       tone that would usually be created by each of these techniques.

a) written in first person ("I think")   ☐

b) lots of opinions   ☐

c) formal language used   ☐

d) lots of facts used   ☐

e) sounds emotional   ☐

f) slang used   ☐

Q2   Decide whether the text below has a personal or an impersonal tone.
       Find two pieces of evidence from the text to support your answer.

> There is a growing feeling that the situation concerning air pollution needs to be addressed.
> The number of individuals suffering from breathing problems in the city has been steadily
> increasing for years, with levels of aerosols and other greenhouse gases reaching record
> levels. Possible solutions are to be discussed at the next city council meeting.

The tone is **personal** / **impersonal** because:

1) ....

2) ....

Q3   Use the following extract from an agony aunt column
       to answer the question at the bottom of the page.

MINI-ESSAY
QUESTION

> Dear Fiona,
>
> You poor thing, you're really down in the dumps, aren't you? I know it's hard to believe but your life
> will improve — you just need to take control over things again. Concentrate on what you used to
> be like, when you were more confident and enjoying life.
>
> One thing that's definitely worth a shot is consulting a career guidance counsellor. If you haven't
> got time for this then there are plenty of books that I can recommend on choosing the right job.
>
> The main thing to remember is that you're the boss of your own life — so take charge!

What techniques does the writer use to create a friendly, personal style in her writing?

Following an Argument

Q1   Writers use many different techniques when they argue a point.
Draw a line to match each of the following techniques with the correct example.

fact   "I strongly believe that we can win the World Cup."

opinion   "Surely you don't believe these disgusting lies?"

implication   "For example, a right angle is 90°."

rhetorical question   "Ever since Mr Hardcastle resigned, Mrs Hardy has been in a good mood."

Q2   Read the following letter to the editor of the *Daily Duncaster* local newspaper.
Then answer the questions that follow.

Dear Sir,

I was horrified to read your article about the new soft drink "Swampy Water" being served in the tuck shop at Duncaster Primary School. This dangerous fad for drinking green, gungy water is clearly idiotic. Firstly, young children might get confused and think it's all right to drink *real* swamp water. I know from my time in the Territorial Army that this can make you very ill indeed. Secondly, "Swampy Water" is full of unhealthy sugar and additives — how else could it be that bright green colour? Last but not least, the drink is expensive and means children don't have money left over to buy normal, healthy snacks. To conclude, "Swampy Water" should be removed from the tuck shop at Duncaster Primary School immediately.

Yours sincerely,
Gerry Bowness

a)   What is the **main** argument of the letter? Tick the correct option below.

☐ Drinking swamp water can make you ill.

☐ "Swampy Water" is unhealthy because it contains additives and sugar.

☐ "Swampy Water" shouldn't be on sale in Duncaster Primary School.

Driver, follow
that argument...

b)   Write down three points the writer makes to support his argument.
Write them using your own words.

1. ....

2. ....

3. ....

8

Evaluating an Argument

Q1   Which of the following would be **bad** to use in an argument? Tick the correct answers.

☐ inconsistencies   ☐ irony

☐ formal tone   ☐ factual inaccuracies

☐ out-of-date examples   ☐ points backed up with examples

☐ confusing explanations   ☐ persuasive language techniques

> Driver, evaluate that argument...
>
> What?

Q2   Read the following texts. Describe one good point and one bad point about the argument in each text.

a)

> The greatest television presenter of all time is Terry Wogan. When he first appeared on television in 1865, Wogan astonished everyone with his energy, enthusiasm and sparkling wit. He had a star quality which all previous television presenters lacked. Who could fail to be charmed by him?

A **good** point about this argument is ....

....

A **bad** point about this argument is ....

....

b)

> As archaeologist David Field says: "There is debate about what ancient stone circles were used for. However, it is almost certain that they had some religious significance." There is strong evidence that many stone circles were religious sites. For example, human and animal bones have been found at Stonehenge. This suggests religious ceremonies were carried out at the site. The evidence is quite weak though.

A **good** point about this argument is ....

....

A **bad** point about this argument is ....

....

Not bad, shame about the ranting...

If you have to analyse an argument, try and think of the reasons why it's effective. It's important to back up your points with examples though. Just saying, "this argument is rubbish," won't do.

Section Two — Following an Argument

Evaluating an Argument

Q1 Read the following text then answer the question that follows.

> I love the colour pink. I love birds. I really love flamingos. How could anyone dislike them? They're the most fascinating, mysterious and beautiful birds in the world! That's why I'm starting a campaign to persuade people to sponsor flamingos in zoos. By donating a few pounds, people can help fund the setting up of breeding programmes for rare flamingo species. The head keeper at my local zoo, Jane Sutton says, "Flamingos really are wonderful creatures. Any donations would be much appreciated."

The table below shows the techniques used by the writer in her argument.
Fill in the table by picking out examples of each technique.

Technique	Example from text
repetition of words / phrases	
rhetorical question	
expert opinion	
exaggeration	

Q2 Read the notice below and answer the question underneath.

Volunteers Needed for Salem Street Neighbourhood Group

No one wants to find litter and dog dirt on the pavement outside the front door. No one wants to have graffiti scratched on the car. No one wants to be woken up in the middle of the night by loud music or people arguing in the street. But, sadly, these things happen all the time in Salem Street. We all deserve to live in a **pleasant, safe, clean** street. And if we join together **we can make it happen**.

- A committee of Salem Street residents is being formed to look at issues like anti-social behaviour, litter and noise levels. It's an opportunity for **us**, the people who live in Salem Street, to be proactive and **improve our community**.

- Similar street committees in the Runford area have proved **very effective** in reducing anti-social behaviour, e.g. Midden Avenue, which used to suffer from high levels of litter and graffiti, is now a very clean, pleasant street.

- Helping with the committee won't take up much of your time — but it will make a **big difference** to Salem Street. Come along and find out more about the committee at our first meeting in **Rixy's Bingo Hall, 8pm, 16th May**.

How well does this notice persuade the reader to join the committee?
Write about:

- examples the writer uses to persuade the reader
- language devices the writer uses

Facts and Opinions

Q1 Write down whether the following statements are opinions or facts.

a) London is the capital city of the UK.

....

b) Glasgow would be a better capital city of Scotland than Edinburgh.

....

Q2 Read the statements below. For each one, say whether you think it is a fact or an opinion and explain your choice.

It's not always clear if something is a fact or an opinion — you have to work it out for yourself.

a) "Water boils at 100 degrees Celsius."

....

....

b) "As Madonna gets older, her music gets better."

....

....

Q3 Read the text below. It was taken from a newspaper article. After you've read it, answer the questions below.

We're All Getting Older

Edward Lightburn

From The Daily Splurge, Thursday 2nd March 2006

We're all living longer and longer. In 1900 in the USA, people could expect to live to around 47 years of age. In 2000 life expectancy had risen to 77 years and the trend is continuing. It might not be long until most people live until they're in their nineties, or even over one hundred.

What are we all going to be doing when we're eighty-something? At the moment, old people don't really get a good deal. As soon as they're too troublesome for their families, they get booted out of home and shipped off to the nearest "care home". And at these places, they'll be patronised, prodded and poked like sick animals: "Does Sarah want her din-dins now? It's her favourite..." It's not something to look forward to, is it?

It used to be that the elderly were respected for their wisdom. Now they're treated like the waste product of society, thrown out and left to rot in their care homes, the landfill sites of modern humanity.

a) Write down one fact and one opinion from the text.

Fact ....

Opinion ....

b) What do you think the author's attitude to old people is? Use evidence from the text to back up your answer.

....

....

....

....

Rhetoric and Bias

Q1   Draw lines to match up each persuasive technique to the sentence which uses it.

a) **rhetorical question**   i)   Nothing is more disgusting than a mouldy sandwich.

b) **repetition of words/phrases** ii) Who on earth would want to eat a mouldy sandwich?

c) **exaggeration**   iii) I hate mould. I hate sandwiches. I really hate mouldy sandwiches.

Q2   Underline whether you think the following texts are biased or unbiased. Explain your answers.

a)
> By far the best hobby for young people is the card game "cribbage". All young people from the ages of eight to eighteen adore playing cribbage. It's easy to learn, doesn't need much equipment and provides hours of fun.

Bias = when the writer's personal opinions affect what he or she writes.

I think the text is **biased / unbiased** because ....

....

....

b)
> In Orkney, you can visit the remains of a Neolithic (Stone Age) village called Skara Brae. The village was inhabited about 5000 years ago. You can see the remains of walls, doorways, fireplaces and stone "furniture".

I think the text is **biased / unbiased** because ....

....

....

Q3   Read the following extract from a travel brochure and answer the question that follows.   MINI-ESSAY QUESTION

Malliwest Resort Hotels

Everyone daydreams. When you're stuck in the office — dealing with tricky customers, struggling with spreadsheets, drinking tepid tea — can you honestly say you haven't dreamt of lying on a sunny beach in a luxury resort, sipping cocktails and being waited on hand and foot?

At Malliwest Resorts you can make your dreams a reality. Only at Malliwest Resorts can you reserve a private beach so that no one else can see what you look like in your swimming costume. Only at Malliwest Resorts can you order your favourite meal and have it made specially. Only at Malliwest Resorts can you ring room service at 4am and get a polite response!

Malliwest Resorts' top priority is to make sure you have the **holiday of a lifetime**. If you book before 20th June, you'll get 15% off the price of your holiday. Surely this is an offer to fulfil anyone's dreams?

How does the writer use language techniques to persuade the reader to visit Malliwest hotels?

Headings

Q1   Label this newspaper front page with the correct terms from the box.

subheading   strapline   headline

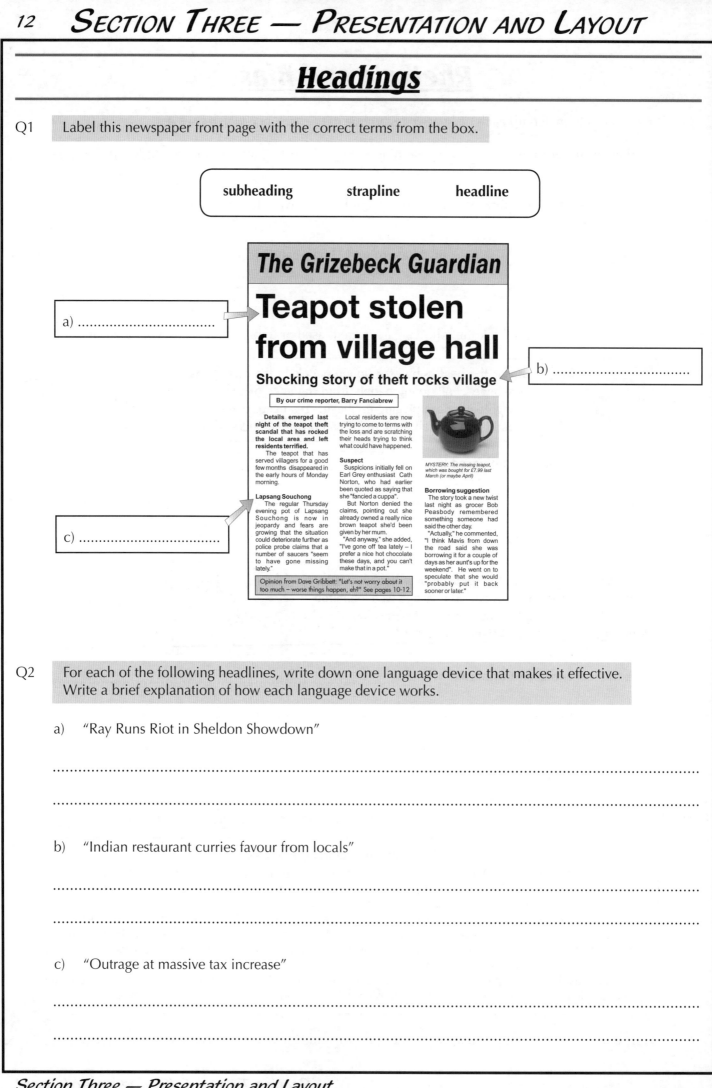

a) ....

b) ....

c) ....

The Grizebeck Guardian

Teapot stolen from village hall

Shocking story of theft rocks village

By our crime reporter, Barry Fanciabrew

Details emerged last night of the teapot theft scandal that has rocked the local area and left residents terrified.
    The teapot that has served villagers for a good few months disappeared in the early hours of Monday morning.

Lapsang Souchong
    The regular Thursday evening pot of Lapsang Souchong is now in jeopardy and fears are growing that the situation could deteriorate further as police probe claims that a number of saucers "seem to have gone missing lately."

Local residents are now trying to come to terms with the loss and are scratching their heads trying to think what could have happened.

Suspect
    Suspicions initially fell on Earl Grey enthusiast Cath Norton, who had earlier been quoted as saying that she "fancied a cuppa".
    But Norton denied the claims, pointing out she already owned a really nice brown teapot she'd been given by her mum.
    "And anyway," she added, "I've gone off tea lately – I prefer a nice hot chocolate these days, and you can't make that in a pot."

MYSTERY: The missing teapot, which was bought for £7.99 last March (or maybe April)

Borrowing suggestion
    The story took a new twist last night as grocer Bob Peasbody remembered something someone had said the other day.
    "Actually," he commented, "I think Mavis from down the road said she was borrowing it for a couple of days as her aunt's up for the weekend". He went on to speculate that she would "probably put it back sooner or later."

Opinion from Dave Gribbett: "Let's not worry about it too much – worse things happen, eh?" See pages 10-12.

Q2   For each of the following headlines, write down one language device that makes it effective. Write a brief explanation of how each language device works.

a)   "Ray Runs Riot in Sheldon Showdown"

....

....

b)   "Indian restaurant curries favour from locals"

....

....

c)   "Outrage at massive tax increase"

....

....

Graphics and Captions

Q1   Briefly explain the intended purpose of each graphic and its caption.

a)   (from a newspaper article
about population growth)

b)   (from a hotel brochure)

World population over the last 500 years

All our rooms are clean,
comfortable and luxurious

a) **Purpose of the population graph and caption**

....

....

....

b) **Purpose of the hotel photo and caption**

....

....

....

Q2   Read the following advertisement for the holiday destination of Montserrat.
How do the headings, photographs and captions help to achieve the text's purpose?

MINI-ESSAY
QUESTION

MONTSERRAT
The Emerald Isle of the Caribbean

Montserrat is a beautiful, lush, green, mountainous island, which Irish
settlers named "the Emerald Isle of the Caribbean". Montserrat lies 27
miles south-west of Antigua, in the Eastern Caribbean chain of islands.

Relax on the island's idyllic,
secluded beaches

The beaches in Montserrat are remarkable in appearance as they have
glistening black sand due to the volcanic nature of the island. They
are some of the most secluded and unspoilt beaches in the world.
For swimming and sunbathing they provide the most calming and
leisurely experience available. The beaches also provide incomparable
surroundings for diving, snorkelling and other water sports.

Learn to dive amid beautiful
unspoilt coral reefs

Section Three — Presentation and Layout

Text Boxes and Columns

Q1 How does the use of columns in the following text add to its effectiveness?

Parrots under threat from pet trade

A British-based conservation organisation has warned that the future of the world's parrots is severely threatened by the international trade for pets.

Thousands of parrots are captured and brought to Europe and North America each year, with many dying during the journey. Neotropical parrots have become one of the most threatened groups of birds in the world, because of international trade and also deforestation of their natural habitats.

This trend is all the more alarming, the organisation says, because until recently parrots have flourished, with numbers on the increase.

....

....

....

Q2 Explain why you think text boxes have been used in the following examples.

a)

Energise, revitalise and relax...
...and work off those extra pounds!

Bring this document to our reception to claim your free 2-week trial voucher (valid until the end of December). You will be entitled to free gym and pool use, exercise classes, social events and loads more!

....

....

b) Here are just two examples of children who have benefited from the generosity of people like you:

Name: Oscar Luis
Age: 9
Story: Oscar used to live in a tin hut in the *barrios* of São Paulo. He now has clean water and basic medical services.

Name: Srinitha
Age: 7
Story: Tiny Srinitha used to beg in the train stations of Delhi. Now she lives in a modest but safe apartment with her foster parents.

....

....

Don't text "columns" and "box" to the examiner...

When you write about layout features like text columns and text boxes, it's not enough just to point them out. You have to <u>explain why</u> the writer has used them and <u>why</u> they are effective.

Bullet Points, Numbered Lists and Colour

Q1   Explain why the use of bullet points or numbered lists is effective in the following texts.

a)

Flu strikes hard and fast. Symptoms may include:
- fever
- aching all over the body
- headache
- dry cough
- lack of appetite
- extreme tiredness.

Do I look like I want to write about bullet points?

....

....

....

b)

Chocolate cake recipe:
1) Lightly grease and line two 20cm wide, 4cm deep sandwich tins.
2) Pre-heat the oven to 180°C / gas mark 4.
3) Beat together the butter, sugar, eggs, flour, baking powder and cocoa.
4) Divide the mixture evenly between the prepared tins.
5) Bake for about 25 minutes, until risen and rich, dark brown.

....

....

....

Q2   What impression do you think a writer would be aiming for by using the following colours?

a) **red** text in a leaflet about road safety

....

....

b) a **pink** background in an advertisement for children's dolls

....

....

c) a **red**, **white** and **blue** colour scheme in a tabloid supplement about a royal wedding

....

....

Fonts

Q1   What impression is created by the following fonts? Explain why you think each font has been used.

a) | Global warming is "worse than previously thought", say Antarctic scientists.

....

....

b) | **Looking for a great day of family fun? Give Franny's Fun Farm a ring!**

....

....

c) | Sometimes you need to take a few risks — and don't underestimate your own abilities...

....

....

Q2   Describe the effects of formatting in the following extracts.

a) | The failing company's chief executive has awarded himself a pay rise of a **whopping £50 000**!

....

....

b) | *Date:* 15th April *Time:* 7.30pm *Place:* Hartnell Square *Event:* World Peace Rally

....

....

"Interesting" is boring...

When you talk about presentational devices it's important you say <u>how</u> they work. It's no good just saying that they make the text more interesting — you have to explain in more detail.

Presentation and Layout — Overview

Q1   Read the text below and then answer the question at the bottom of the page.

Eat Superfoods to Give Your Health a Boost

Eat superfoods to give your health a boost — we tell you how...

By Tyler Steele, the Daily Splurge's food writer

If your New Year's resolution to live more healthily hasn't taken off yet, don't panic — here are some of the top "superfoods", as recommended by dieticians:

• **Carrots** provide beta-carotene, which can reduce the risk of stroke.

• **Chilli peppers** can help to reduce cholesterol and protect you from cancer.

• **Tomatoes** stimulate immune functions.

• **Citrus fruits** are an excellent source of vitamin C, which helps your body fight cancers.

Health experts are keen to point out, though, that in addition to a balanced and nutritious diet, a healthy lifestyle must also include regular exercise. A good mixture of aerobic and anaerobic exercise taken three times a week is a good general guide.

"Exercise" doesn't have to mean getting up at 5am every day and running a half marathon! Something as easy as a brisk 30 minute walk every day can make a big contribution to improved health.

Write down four presentational devices the writer uses in the leaflet and explain why they are effective.

1. ....

....

....

2. ....

....

....

3. ....

....

....

4. ....

....

....

Descriptive Language

Q1   Write down what the word "imagery" means.

....

....

Q2   Writers sometimes use the five senses (sight, touch, smell, sound and taste) to describe things. Circle which of the five senses is being used in each of the following descriptions.

a)   "They were drawn to the kitchen by the familiar, welcoming scent of freshly-baked bread."

sight   touch   smell   sound   taste

b)   "The glass eye felt cold and smooth like a pebble."

sight   touch   smell   sound   taste

* Adjectives are describing words.

Q3   Underline the adjectives* in the following description.

"I had five tedious hours to wait at Singapore's shiny, modern airport. While my bulging holdall rested at my tired, sandalled feet, I observed the curious surroundings. An interesting mix of travellers bustled by: excited families, overweight businessmen, dirty young backpackers. My nostrils detected the heavenly scent of fresh croissants and strong coffee wafting from the over-priced eateries. I felt a slight chill and dry mouth from the air conditioning, yet was grateful: better to be sitting in a fake, cool breeze than wilting outside under the burning sun."

Q4   Read the text below, then answer the questions in the boxes.

MINI-ESSAY QUESTION

From *Memories of Aldport*, by Geoff Buckley

I visited the old, ghostly railway station down the road from where I grew up. The grey, rusty bridge sparked countless memories of days gone by — the thunderous roar of an approaching train echoing down the track like a warning of an alien invasion.

The fact that nothing passes under the bridge any more adds to the eerie atmosphere the station has now. I would like to take a stroll along the railway track's forbidding, overgrown lines — but the combination of the unnecessary barbed wire fence and the thick, thorny bushes which try to trip you up, sadly makes this impossible.

a)   How does the writer of this text feel about the railway station he describes?

b)   What writing techniques are used to describe the station and trains? What impression do they create?

Metaphors and Similes

Q1   Draw lines to link each term with its correct definition:

a) **metaphor**   A comparison where the writer says that something is something else.

b) **simile**   A comparison where the writer says something is similar
to something else, often using the words "like" or "as".

Q2   For each phrase, say whether it is a metaphor or a simile.

a) | John's as thick as two short planks. | →   ....

b) | Her eyes were X-rays, penetrating my soul. | →   ....

c) | Jane was a tower of strength. | →   ....

d) | I was stuck like a lettuce in a teapot. | →   ....

Q3   What impression is created by the following simile?

| When hunky Brad Depp walked into the room, Jane blushed as red as a beetroot. |

....

....

....

Q4   What impression is created by the following metaphor?

| Jane's heart was a block of ice which melted when she kissed hunky Brad Depp. |

....

....

....

I know the writer quite well — I metaphor times...

Make sure you've got these terms worked out in your head before the exam. Metaphors and similes are similar but you need to learn the difference between them.

Personification, Alliteration and Onomatopoeia

Q1   Fill in the blanks in the following sentences.

a) .... means repeating the same sound at the start of words in a phrase.

b) .... means describing something as if it is a person or animal.

c) .... means using a word that sounds like what it is describing.

Q2   For each extract, write down the technique being used and give an example from the extract. Then say what effect the technique used creates.

a) "The computer squawked into life before cheerily informing me that I had performed an illegal operation."

....

....

....

b) "The thumping beats on offer at the venue now are a different world from the Oompah tunes of old."

....

....

....

c) "Bag a Bargain at Brigson's — Portsmouth's Premier Pig Farm!"

....

....

....

Q3   Read the following extract from a travel book then answer the question that follows. MINI-ESSAY QUESTION

> The streets of Kuala Lumpur are a labyrinth of lost lanes, back-streets, dead-ends and confusing alleys which double-back on themselves. An apparently endless series of haphazard side streets breaks out from the main street of the Chinatown area like snakes winding across the desert. On every corner hang the strong but irresistible smells of food stalls offering an abundance of exotic cuisines.
>
> The low growl of heavy trucks and buzzing of the thousands of scooters that swarm the streets like bees made my dreams of a bit of peace and quiet ridiculously optimistic. The sticky heat combined with choking exhaust fumes and loud noise certainly made for a vibrant but less than relaxing atmosphere.

What writing techniques does the writer of this text use to make his descriptions vivid and effective?

<u>*Irony and Sarcasm*</u>

Q1   Draw lines to match each definition to the correct term.

a)   Language that is mocking or nasty.   **irony**

b)   Saying one thing but meaning another.   **sarcasm**

Q2   What is the effect of the writer's sarcastic tone in this article about extending pub licensing hours?

> **From *Unhappy Hour* by Jane Green**
>
> Of course, the solution to binge-drinking is perfectly clear: we should keep pubs open all day long. This way, everyone will get bored of the idea of beer and take up knitting instead. I can picture it now: the young louts who terrorise our streets will surely all turn to each other and say, "Do you know what, Jeremy? This drinking lark just isn't the fun it used to be when we got cleared out by 11 — I'm seriously considering my life options".

....

....

....

....

....

Q3   How does the writer of the following extract use irony to express his opinion?   MINI-ESSAY QUESTION

> **From *Customer Disservice — modern day madness* by Mel Sage**
>
> The other day I had to phone up my insurance company with the horrendously complicated problem of changing my address. After spending 20 thrilling minutes on hold listening to a variety of boy bands performing their hits, I finally got through to the man who could help me — Wayne.
>
> However, there was a slight hitch. Wayne informed me that he was having some "technical problems", which was obviously of great comfort to me, as I watched night time slowly approach and began to revise my plans for what was left of the week.

Technical and Emotive Language

Q1 For each language feature, fill in the box with a **T** if it's used in technical language or an **E** if it's used in emotive language.

a) statistics ☐

b) exaggeration ☐

c) strong opinions ☐

d) rhetorical questions ☐

Q2 Find two examples of emotive language in the following text, taken from a leaflet published by an environmental group. For each example, describe what effect it creates.

> What kind of future do we want to give our children? Do we want them to have fresh air to breathe? Do we want a clean, safe environment they can enjoy and share with their own children?
>
> Or do we want a filthy, concrete planet with nothing left of our once green and pleasant land, where trees are just something fondly recalled by our grandparents?
>
> The answer is surely obvious. Yet if we allow the situation to carry on as it is now, with mass deforestation and over-development in the world's most fragile environments, we're heading for disaster. We must take action now if we have any hopes of avoiding this catastrophe.

1. ....

....

....

2. ....

....

....

Q3 Why does the writer use technical language in this extract about weather and climate?

> The United Kingdom has a temperate maritime climate, with most lowland areas receiving between 500 and 1000mm of annual rainfall. Annual temperatures are generally between 5 and 15°C, with urban areas up to 5°C warmer than rural areas, due to the urban heat island effect. The south is also warmer than the north, due to higher levels of insolation*.

* Insolation is radiation from the sun that heats the planet.

....

....

....

....

Tabloid Newspaper Language

Q1   Fill in the table below using examples from the following tabloid newspaper article.

Tubby Teddy's "inbred" gag is no laughing matter

Portly TV funny-man Ted Chance has outraged residents of Sollingford by ignorantly slamming them all as "inbred yokels who think gurning is great entertainment".

He made the offensive quip at a comedy festival last week and has left the town fuming. Locals have since made it clear there's fat Chance Ted will be welcome in the town from now on.

Local man Paul Drake launched a stinging attack on Chance's comments, saying: "The man's just shown how ignorant he is. *He should stop and think before he opens his big fat mouth.*"

Defence

The "Cheeky Chancer" tried to defend his gag yesterday, claiming it was tongue-in-cheek. He retorted: "I don't think anyone would have thought twice about it if they hadn't been so touchy."

Language type	Example
biased language	
emotive language	
slang	
nicknames	
puns	

Q2   Describe how the following extracts from *The Daily Rubbish* try to attract the reader's interest.

a) Outspoken TV host Terry Bar has once again left his TV bosses red-faced with embarrassment. On his show 'Terry Talk', terrible Terry lashed out grumpily at celeb chef Greg Ruben.

....

....

....

b) *It's time to stand up for common sense!* Join *The Daily Rubbish*'s campaign and together we can put an end to this nonsense.

....

....

....

Structure

Q1   Circle the features that you would usually expect to find in the body text of an article.

summary of the
main points

opinions

headlines

separate paragraphs

bylines

specific details

statistics

Q2   The following extracts have all been taken from the same newspaper article. For each one, say whether you think it is from the introduction, the body of the article, or the conclusion. Explain your answers.

a)

> Many motorists are in favour of the new trial scheme, seeing it as a simple, common-sense solution that will reduce traffic jams. But critics are concerned that, when the hard shoulder is being used for normal traffic, there will no longer be a safe place for broken-down vehicles to await rescue.

....

....

b)

> The main issue is whether this can effectively reduce congestion without adding to accident rates. If it can, it is likely to prove much more popular than other methods, such as toll roads. If the scheme proves successful, it could be introduced to motorways up and down the country.

....

....

c)

> A controversial new scheme to avoid traffic congestion on one of Britain's busiest roads has divided opinion among motorists and road safety groups. The strategy, on trial from this week, allows drivers to use the hard shoulder when the amount of traffic is at its highest.

....

....

Every bit of the article is important

Although they contain less information than the body text, the introduction and conclusion are very important. The intro gets the readers' interest, and the conclusion is what will stick in their minds.

P.E.E.

Q1 In an exam answer, which of the following could you **not** use as an example to back up a point? Circle the correct answer.

a) A quote from the text.

b) A fact or statistic from the text.

c) Your opinion of the subject of the text.

d) A description of the presentation of the text.

Q2 Read the following exam answers. Tick the answers which use the P.E.E. technique (Point, Example, Explanation).

a) The writer uses similes to make his description of Kidston's motor racing more vivid. For example, he describes Kidston's Bentley as being "like a cheetah". This shows how powerful and fast Kidston's car was.

☐

b) The writer says the racing driver Glen Kidston was glamorous and charming. He had an affair with the young Barbara Cartland. In 1931, he died tragically in a plane crash in the Drakensberg Mountains.

☐

c) The writer uses the headline of the magazine article to capture readers' attention. It describes Glen Kidston as "Britain's Forgotten Hero". This sounds glamorous and mysterious and would intrigue readers.

☐

Q3 Read the following extract from a tourist information sheet and answer the question that follows.

> Avebury Visitor Centre: Information Sheet 5
> **West Kennet Long Barrow — The Skeleton Tomb**
>
> West Kennet Long Barrow is an ancient chambered tomb near Avebury. There are five chambers (rooms) in the tomb. It is safe to go inside the tomb to look at the chambers. When the tomb was excavated, different types of skeleton were found in each chamber:
> • Male adult skeletons were found in the main chamber, opposite the entrance.
> • Children's skeletons were found in the chamber to the left of the entrance.
> • The skeletons of elderly people were found in the chamber to the right of the entrance.
> • A mixture of male and female adult skeletons were found in the two other chambers.

Explain how the writer has used a presentational device to make the text more effective. Use the P.E.E. framework below to help you answer the question.

Point ....

....

Example ....

....

Explanation ....

....

....

Writing in Paragraphs

Q1   Circle the words and phrases which would be useful for linking paragraphs together.

Another point of view is   Also   Secondly

Although   The writer says

In addition to this   In the summer

However   On the other hand

Q2   Read the following exam answers. The student hasn't linked his paragraphs together well. Rewrite each of the exam answers (a-d), so that the paragraphs are linked smoothly together.

You'll need to write your answers to this question on separate paper.

a)   The writer uses several presentational devices to make the article more effective. One example is the headline, which is in a large, bold font. This grabs the reader's attention immediately when he or she sees the article.
    The background colour of the article is grey. This emphasises the sombre tone of the article. Muted colours like grey are associated with serious subjects.

b)   The writer uses language devices to make her argument more persuasive. Firstly, she uses the rhetorical question "Who would want an axe-murderer living next door?" to encourage the reader to identify with her point of view.
    The writer uses a metaphor to describe her opinion: "this situation is a slippery eel which might twist out of our grasp". This creates a vivid image of the difficulty of the situation.

c)   The first text argues in favour of school uniforms. For example, it describes them as "a symbol of unity and school identity" which implies a traditional, positive viewpoint.
    The second text argues against school uniforms. It describes them as "a fashion disaster" and "an embarrassment to pupils". This suggests a very negative opinion.

d)   The book extract is aimed at an audience of primary school children. It includes simple pictures to explain how to use a camera. This makes it easy for children to understand.
    The magazine article is aimed at adults who are interested in photography. It uses technical vocabulary such as "developer" and "focus" which shows it's written for photography enthusiasts.

Link your paragraphs together smoothly...

Learn a few of those <u>handy little phrases</u> for linking paragraphs. They're the kind of thing that examiners look out for — they show you've thought about your writing.

Reading with Insight

Q1   Draw lines to match up each sentence (a-d) with the type of tone it conveys (i-iv).

a) I was disgusted by the badly-researched, shabby journalism displayed by your newspaper's coverage of the event.

b) The MP Gareth Soames visited the County Hospital on Thursday 11th December to open a new ward.

c) Gary Barlow's dancing drew gasps of wonder from the crowd — the rumours were true, he really had improved!

d) There's nothing I love more than queueing in a really long traffic jam on a boiling hot day — it's fantastic.

i) **light-hearted tone**

ii) **sarcastic tone**

iii) **serious tone**

iv) **angry tone**

Q2   Read the following text and answer the questions which follow.

> The films Alfred Hitchcock made in the 1950s and 1960s contain glimpses of greatness. Images from these films have become famous, for example Janet Leigh screaming in the shower in 'Psycho'.
>
> However, when looking at Hitchcock's career as a whole, it is his earlier films from the 1930s and 1940s which are the most enjoyable. Early films like 'The 39 Steps' and 'The Lady Vanishes' are very funny and have a great lightness of touch. In contrast, his later films, even classics like 'Vertigo' and 'The Birds', are often slow and humourless.
>
> One reason for the change in quality of Hitchcock's films was the way he started to be treated as an important, "auteur*" director as he got older. Younger film directors like François Truffaut worshipped him. This swelled Hitchcock's already large ego, and meant his style of film-making became more pretentious and dull. Stories from the 1950s and 1960s about his bullying, possessive attitude towards young actresses like Tippi Hedren also raise doubts about his professionalism in his later years.
>
> So my advice is: settle down on the sofa to watch some of those early, off-the-cuff Hitchcock masterpieces — and leave the later "classics" for nerdy film students.
>
> _* auteur = when a director of a film is so important that they are considered to be the author of the film_

a) Pick out words and phrases from the text to complete the table below.

Words and phrases which imply the writer dislikes Hitchcock's later films	Words and phrases which imply the writer likes Hitchcock's early films	Words and phrases which imply the writer dislikes Hitchcock as a person
1.	1.	1.
2.	2.	2.

b) In this text, the writer describes how much he likes Alfred Hitchcock's early films. Briefly describe something you feel similarly enthusiastic about.

....

....

....

....

__Search and Find Questions__

Q1   Read the text below.

> "Last weekend we found ourselves with nothing to do on a warm, sunny day, so decided on a trip to the zoo. The entrance to the zoo was via a rusty iron gate that looked in serious need of repair. The ground was covered in litter. I thought things might improve once we were inside, but unfortunately I was wrong: the majority of the animals looked malnourished and miserable in their enclosures, which all seemed dull and empty, with nothing for the animals to do and precious little space for them to run around in. All in all, it was a pretty depressing place."

List five things you learn about the zoo that suggest it is badly run.

1. ....

2. ....

3. ....

4. ....

5. ....

Q2   Read the text below.

> I just can't understand the popularity of hip hop. Hardly any of it's original, and it's just far too easy to make. Whereas rock music involves real instruments that need skilled musicians, hip hop's created mainly on a computer, and often from recycled bits of somebody else's music. I'm not saying that anyone could do it, but I can't believe it's particularly difficult.

Write down **three phrases** from the text that would help to answer the question: "Why does the writer think that rock music is better than hip hop?"

1. ....

....

2. ....

....

3. ....

....

Comparing Texts

Q1   Read the following two texts and answer the questions which follow.

Linda's Problem Page — answers your most embarrassing problems!!!

I farted in front of him!

Dear Linda,

There's a boy at school I really like. He sat next to me in a Maths lesson and I was really excited cos I thought he might fancy me. But I farted and he hasn't talked to me since. What can I do? Love Zoe xxxxxx

Linda says....

Hi Zoe,

Oops! How embarrassing! Don't worry though. Silly moments like this happen to all of us. If this boy really likes you, he won't let one fart get in the way of a relationship. My advice is: be confident, and go and talk to him next time you see him. You'll both soon forget all about it. Good luck! Linda.

Write to Linda c/o 'Girl!' magazine, PO Box 5058

Personal Financial Advice: Case Study

Case Study: Ms Barber, 35, single, no children
Salary: £18,000 per year
Savings: £14,500 in a savings account
Pension: Contributes 8% of her salary to a private pension.
Property: 1 bed flat, mortgage £290/month.
Debt: Credit card debt £2100

The Daily Missive's financial advisor, Greg Smith writes Ms Barber should pay off her credit card debt using part of her savings. She's likely to be paying more interest on her credit card debt than she is earning on her savings, so she's currently losing money.

Secondly, Ms Barber should find out whether her employer would be prepared to make contributions to her pension, which would improve her pension fund.

---

a)   Complete the following table with notes about the two texts.

	Linda's Problem Page	Personal Financial Advice
Audience of text		
Purpose of text		
Tone of text		
Main language devices used		
Main presentational devices used		

b)   Compare how each text uses language and presentational devices.   MINI-ESSAY QUESTION

My text is toned, tanned and looking fabulous...

You're rattling through the book now — only the exam section left to go. Don't worry about that — it might look like a tiger, but it's really just a harmless tabby cat. Ahh.

Sample Exam — Questions

In this section, you get to be the examiner. You'll look at some students' answers to exam questions and decide what marks they should get. It'll help you understand what examiners are looking for — which will improve the quality of your own answers. Here's how it works:

1) Read the sample exam questions and texts on pages 30-33. They're similar in style to the ones you'll get in Section A of your Unit 1 GCSE English Language or GCSE English exam. Make sure you understand the questions and texts. You don't have to answer the questions.

2) Then on pages 34-43 there are mark schemes explaining how to mark each question. And there are some student answers which you have to mark.

Here are the sample exam questions. Remember — this time, you don't have to answer the questions. Phew.

Read **Item 1**, the article called *Climate change explained* and answer the questions below.

1 List 4 of the impacts of climate change that are mentioned in the article.

(4 marks)

2 From the article, what do you learn about how and why the climate changes?

(4 marks)

Now read **Item 2**, the article called *Roger Federer — the tennis ace who's smashed every record in the book* and answer the question below.

3 What reasons can you find in the article for saying that Roger Federer is generous and 'the greatest tennis player of all time'?

(8 marks)

Now read **Item 3**, *First day* and answer the question below.

4 How does the writer use language to show his feelings and to inform the reader about what is happening?

(12 marks)

Now look again at all three items. They have each been presented in a different way.

5 Choose **two** of these items. Compare them using these headings:
- the titles and subheadings
- the pictures / diagrams and captions

(12 marks)

And tonight Matthew — I will be The Examiner...

Enjoy being an examiner while you can. Cherish the feeling of power... Buy a red pen... On p.44 your examiner status will be taken away and you'll have to answer the questions again. Drat.

Sample Exam — Item 1

Here's Item 1 for the questions on page 30. It's an article from the Environment Agency website.

Climate change explained

Climate is not the same as weather

Climate is the average weather in a region over a long period, usually 30 years. It includes temperature, wind and rainfall patterns. The Earth's climate has changed many times in the past — this is known as 'natural variability'.

The greenhouse effect

The Earth is kept warm by greenhouse gases such as carbon dioxide and methane, which are naturally found in the atmosphere. They trap heat in the atmosphere and keep our planet warm enough to inhabit. Without greenhouse gases the Earth would be about −18 degrees Celsius.

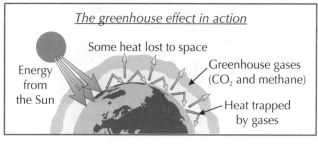

The greenhouse effect in action

Some heat lost to space

Energy from the Sun

Greenhouse gases (CO_2 and methane)

Heat trapped by gases

Human impact on climate

In the last 150 years, human activity, mostly the burning of fossil fuels (coal, oil and gas), has resulted in the release of large amounts of greenhouse gases into the atmosphere. This is enhancing the greenhouse effect and pushing up global temperature.

Average global temperature has risen approximately 1°C in the last 100 years, and even if we stopped emitting greenhouse gases tomorrow, it would continue to rise by at least 0.6°C.

There are clear signs that our world is warming. Ice sheets and glaciers are melting and average river water temperatures are increasing. Globally, the ten hottest years on record have all been since 1997.

How will the climate change?

While a two degree rise in average global temperature doesn't sound very dangerous, the effects will be stark. The present one degree rise has already had a severe impact. Antarctica is losing around 190 billion tonnes of ice a year. Eighty percent of the Maldives lies three feet or less above sea level and the predicted rise in sea level caused by global warming could wipe the country off the map. Impacts of further warming of four degrees or more are likely to include:

- big reductions in food production in some regions
- hundreds of millions of people without enough water
- mass species extinctions
- sea level rising by several metres

How will it affect us?

In the UK, there could be more extreme weather events, such as flooding, storms and drought as well as wetter warmer winters and hotter drier summers.

Sample Exam — Item 2

This is Item 2 to go with the exam questions on page 30. It's an article about the Swiss tennis player Roger Federer.

Roger Federer — the tennis ace who's smashed every record in the book

Roger Federer holding the winner's trophy from the Australian Open 2010

Roger Federer is a Swiss tennis player. He's considered by many former players to be the greatest tennis player of all time.

Born to play tennis

Federer was born in Switzerland on the 8th of August 1981. He started playing tennis at the age of 8, and left home at 14 to go to a Swiss tennis academy. He turned professional in 1998 after winning the boys' singles and doubles titles at Wimbledon. He is married to former tennis player Mirka Vavrinec, and became a father to twin girls in July 2009.

On top of the tennis world

So far, Federer has won a record 16 Grand Slam* singles titles. He won at Wimbledon for five years in a row between 2003 and 2007, then again in 2009. He has won the US Open five times, the Australian Open four times and the French Open once. Because he's won Grand Slam titles on all three types of surface (clay, grass and hard courts) he's thought of as the all-round greatest tennis player — other great players have been specialists on only one type of surface. Federer holds the record for the highest number of consecutive weeks spent as number 1 in the ATP (Association of Tennis Professionals) ranking — 237 weeks. He's also received the Laureus World Sportsman of the Year Award four times, from 2005 to 2008.

Roger Federer meets a young fan

Champion for charities

In 2003, Federer set up the Roger Federer Foundation, which promotes sport for young people in Switzerland and helps to improve education for some of the poorest people in Africa. He has been a Goodwill Ambassador for UNICEF* since 2006, visiting places like Tamil Nadu in India, which was badly affected by a tsunami in 2004. Federer has also raised a lot of money to help people affected by other natural disasters. He auctioned off his racquet from the US Open in 2005, and donated the money raised to the people affected by Hurricane Katrina. At the Australian Open in 2010 he organised a charity event called 'Hit for Haiti', which raised money for victims of the 2010 Haiti earthquake.

*Grand Slam — the Grand Slam tennis tournaments are the four most important competitions held each year.
*UNICEF — the United Nations Children's Fund

Sample Exam — Item 3

And here's Item 3 for the exam questions on page 30. In this extract, Roald Dahl (the famous children's writer) is remembering being left at boarding school for the first time.

First day
St Peter's, 1925-9 (age 9-13)

So off we set, my mother and I and my trunk and my tuck-box, and we boarded the paddle-steamer and went swooshing across the Bristol Channel in a shower of spray. I liked that part of it, but I began to grow apprehensive as I disembarked on to the pier at Weston-super-Mare and watched my trunk and tuck-box being loaded into an English taxi which would drive us to St Peter's. I had absolutely no idea what was in store for me. I had never spent a single night away from our large family before.

St Peter's was on a hill above the town. It was a long three-storeyed stone building that looked rather like a private lunatic asylum, and in front of it lay the playing-fields with their three football pitches. One-third of the building was reserved for the Headmaster and his family. The rest of it housed the boys, about one hundred and fifty of them altogether, if I remember rightly.

As we got out of the taxi, I saw the whole driveway abustle with small boys and their parents and their trunks and their tuck-boxes, and a man I took to be the Headmaster was swimming around among them shaking everybody by the hand.

I have already told you that *all* Headmasters are giants, and this one was no exception. He advanced upon my mother and shook her by the hand, then he shook me by the

hand and as he did so he gave me the kind of flashing grin a shark might give to a small fish just before he gobbles it up. One of his front teeth, I noticed, was edged all the way round with gold, and his hair was slicked down with so much hair-cream that it glistened like butter.

'Right,' he said to me. 'Off you go and report to the Matron.' And to my mother he said briskly, 'Goodbye, Mrs Dahl. I shouldn't linger if I were you. We'll look after him.'

My mother got the message. She kissed me on the cheek and said goodbye and climbed right back into the taxi.

The Headmaster moved away to another group and I was left standing there beside my brand new trunk and my brand new tuck-box. I began to cry.

the Loony Bin!

Mark Scheme — Question 1

This page gives you <u>advice</u> and a <u>mark scheme</u> for marking question 1 of the sample exam. Read this information and digest it. Chew carefully and don't rush — you don't want to get indigestion. Then you'll be ready for marking the student answers on p.35.

'List' questions are pretty straightforward

1) All you need to do for this one is pick out <u>four impacts of climate change</u> from the text.

2) For questions like this, you'll be given <u>four numbered lines</u> to write your answer on. Just put <u>one point</u> on <u>each line</u>. Easy.

3) It's a good idea to <u>scan through</u> the text and <u>circle</u> the different impacts of climate change as you go. Then all you need to do is <u>write out</u> the impacts you've circled.

Paul was thirty years old and had written five books about climate change before he realised the question was only worth 4 marks.

4) You should use <u>quotation marks</u> when you copy bits of the text, or you can just write out the impacts in your <u>own words</u>.

5) Make sure you don't write the <u>same</u> impact twice though — you'll only get a mark for each <u>different</u> point you make.

6) You <u>don't</u> have to worry about P.E.E. as the question only needs short answers, but make sure your <u>spelling</u> and <u>punctuation</u> are right.

Use this table to mark question 1

The table below shows some of the points that could be picked out of the text to answer this question. Of course, you only need to get four as there are only 4 marks to get.

Number of marks	Possible points
1 mark for each point made, up to a maximum of 4	• "Ice sheets and glaciers are melting." • "Average river water temperatures are increasing." • Antarctica has been "losing around 190 billion tonnes of ice a year". • Climate change could cause "big reductions in food production in some regions". • It could leave "hundreds of millions of people without enough water". • Climate change could lead to "mass species extinctions". • There could be more extreme weather events in the UK. • The UK could have "wetter warmer winters and hotter drier summers". • The sea level could rise "by several metres". • Rising sea level could wipe out the Maldives.

A good mark — check out his Gospel for more...

These straightforward questions are an easy way to bag the first few marks in the exam. As long as you do plenty of practice you shouldn't find it too hard to get most of the marks on offer.

Sample Answers — Question 1

Now it's your turn to be the <u>examiner</u>. This can be <u>tricky</u> but it's really <u>useful</u> if you can do it.

1) Make sure you've read the advice and table on page 34.

2) Use the mark scheme to <u>mark</u> the answers to question 1 below.

3) <u>Explain</u> how you've decided on the marks in the lines below the answers.

4) The <u>first one's been done for you</u> to show you what to do.

Write notes around the answer — that's what the real examiners do.

> Read **Item 1**, the article called *Climate change explained* and answer the question below.
>
> **1** List 4 of the impacts of climate change that are mentioned in the article.
>
> *(4 marks)*

Answer 1

Q1
1. Climate and weather are different things.
2. Climate is actually the average weather over a long period of time.
3. It is also about temperature and the wind and the rain.
4.

This answer gets ⬚ 0 marks out of 4 because ...it doesn't include any points that are relevant to... the question.

These two are for you to mark...

Answer 2

Q1
1. Climate change could make lots of species of animals become extinct.
2. "Ice sheets and glaciers are melting".
3. It's important that we learn about climate change to understand what it is and what it does.
4. People need to do something about climate change otherwise there will be serious consequences.

This answer gets ⬚ marks out of 4 because ....
....
....

Answer 3

Q1
1. Climate change could leave "millions of people without enough water".
2. Sea level could rise "by several metres".
3. Places like the Maldives could be wiped out completely.
4. In the UK, we might have "more extreme weather events", like storms, flooding and droughts.

This answer gets ⬚ marks out of 4 because ....
....
....

Mark Scheme — Question 2

Here's advice and a mark scheme for marking question 2. Read all this info through — then you'll be prepared for marking the sample student answers on the next page.

You have to write about how and why the climate changes

1) Question 2 is worth the same amount of marks as question 1, so you should spend the <u>same amount of time</u> on it.

2) You need to focus on the <u>ways</u> in which the climate changes, and <u>why</u> this happens.

3) Explain your points in your <u>own words</u> and use <u>short quotes</u> to back up what you say.

Look for good points like these when you're marking

This question asks you to pick out some <u>important points</u> from the article. Read the article <u>in detail</u> from <u>start to finish</u>. A good answer could include the following points:

- There's "natural variability" in the Earth's climate — it's changed lots of times in the past.
- Greenhouse gases (e.g. carbon dioxide and methane) keep the Earth warm by trapping heat in the atmosphere.
- Greenhouse gases occur naturally, but large amounts have been released into the atmosphere in the last 150 years.
- Human activity, such as the burning of fossil fuels, produces lots of greenhouse gases.
- The increase in greenhouse gases means the Earth's temperature is rising.
- Global temperature has risen by 1°C over the last 100 years.

Mark question 2 like this

Look at the table below to see what an answer needs to be like for each mark band. When you're marking an answer, look at this table and work out which descriptions <u>fit the answer best</u>, then award the mark you think it <u>deserves</u> from the mark band.

Number of marks	What's been written	How it's written	How the answer's put together
Band 1 1 mark	Not much written. Might make one simple point.	Confusingly written, might copy out sections of the text.	No clear structure.
Band 2 2-3 marks	Two or three points that show how and why the climate changes.	Some use of own words. Fairly clearly written.	Attempt at structure, but not always kept to.
Band 3 4 marks	Clear explanation of how and why the climate changes, using good examples to back up points.	Confidently and clearly written in own words.	Well structured answer, with points linked together so that it flows well.

Sample Answers — Question 2

Now it's time to have a go at marking answers to question 2. Don't be too harsh...

1) Read the mark scheme on page 36.
2) Use the mark scheme to <u>mark</u> the answers below to question 2.
3) Then <u>explain</u> why you gave those marks in the lines below the answers.

It's how you explain your marking that's the important bit.

> Read **Item 1**, the article called *Climate change explained* and answer the question below.
>
> 2   From the article, what do you learn about how and why the climate changes?
>
> *(4 marks)*

Answer 1

Q2   The climate changes because the burning of fossil fuels (coal, oil and gas) has resulted in the release of large amounts of greenhouse gases into the atmosphere.

This answer gets [ ] marks out of 4 because ....

....

....

....

....

Answer 2

Q2   Greenhouse gases trap heat in the atmosphere. But "human activity" like burning oil, coal and gas has produced lots of greenhouse gases, so the Earth is getting hotter because there are more greenhouse gases in the atmosphere.

This answer gets [ ] marks out of 4 because ....

....

....

....

....

This room is like a greenhouse...

How are you finding being the examiner? If you really like it, you could always do a degree in English, then a PGCE teacher qualification and then apply to be one for real... Takes a while though.

Mark Scheme — Question 3

Hopefully you'll be getting the hang of it by now. Read through the advice and mark scheme on this page, then mark the answers on p.39.

Question 3 is worth 8 marks, so it needs a longer answer

1) Read the article <u>carefully</u> before starting your answer.

2) This answer needs to be <u>balanced</u> — you need to talk about why Federer is <u>generous</u> and why he's '<u>the greatest tennis player of all time</u>'. Try and write about the <u>same amount</u> for each part of the question.

3) The space for your answer will be <u>divided up</u> into sections for the two parts of the question, making it easy to <u>structure</u> your writing.

4) Use <u>short quotes</u> from the text to back up your points — don't just copy big chunks of it out.

Look for good points like these when you're marking

<u>Generous</u>

- He set up the Roger Federer Foundation which "helps to improve education" for poor people in Africa.
- He has given up his time to be a "Goodwill Ambassador for UNICEF".
- He auctioned his racquet to raise money for the victims of Hurricane Katrina.
- In 2010, he raised money for victims of the Haiti earthquake by organising a "charity event called 'Hit for Haiti'".

<u>'The greatest tennis player of all time'</u>

- He has won "a record 16 Grand Slam singles titles".
- He won Wimbledon for "five years in a row between 2003 and 2007", then he won it "again in 2009".
- He has won Grand Slam titles on all three types of surface.
- He holds the record for the highest number of consecutive weeks as the number one player.
- He has won an award for being the "World Sportsman of the Year" four times.

Mark question 3 like this

Use the table below to find out what kind of answer would get each mark.

Number of marks	What's been written	How it's written	How the answer's put together
Band 1 1-2 marks	Not much written. One or two basic points made.	Confusingly written, might copy out sections of the text.	No clear structure.
Band 2 3-5 marks	Some good points made about why Federer is both generous and a great tennis player.	Quite clearly written, mainly uses own words.	Some attempt at structure by linking points together, but not always kept to.
Band 3 6-8 marks	Several points made about why Federer is both generous and a great tennis player, backed up by good examples from the text.	Clearly and confidently written, using own words throughout.	Well structured answer with points linked together, making it easy to follow.

Sample Answers — Question 3

More marking for you to do on this page. Remember to write "v.g." on the good answers...

1) Read the mark scheme on page 38 and use it to <u>mark</u> these answers to question 3.

2) Then <u>explain</u> why you gave those marks in the lines below the answers.

Now read **Item 2**, the article called *Roger Federer — the tennis ace who's smashed every record in the book* and answer the question below.

3 What reasons can you find in the article for saying that Roger Federer is generous and 'the greatest tennis player of all time'?

(8 marks)

Answer 1

Q3   <u>Generous</u>
    Roger Federer is generous because he gives lots of money to charity. '<u>The greatest tennis player of all time'</u>
    Roger Federer is considered the greatest player of all time. He won at Wimbledon for five years in a row between 2003 and 2007, then again in 2009. He has won the US Open five times, the Australian Open four times and the French Open once. The article tells us that Federer has won matches on three types of surface "clay, grass and hard courts" and that is why he's the greatest tennis player.

This answer gets ☐ marks out of 8 because ....

....

....

....

Answer 2

Q3   <u>Generous</u>
    Roger Federer is a generous man because he has done lots of things for charity. He set up the "Roger Federer Foundation" to help people in Switzerland and Africa, and he's "a Goodwill Ambassador" for UNICEF.
<u>'The greatest tennis player of all time'</u>
    The title of the article gives one reason why Federer could be described as "the greatest tennis player of all time". It tells us that he's "smashed every record in the book", which means that he is a record breaker. A large number of achievements are also listed, including winning at Wimbledon six times and winning the Australian Open four times. One of the things that makes him really stand out as being better than all the other players though, is that he has won championships "on all three types of surface". This is really unusual as other great tennis players have been really good on clay, grass or hard courts, but not all three.

This answer gets ☐ marks out of 8 because ....

....

....

....

Mark Scheme — Question 4

This is the second-to-last question — and it's worth a lot of marks.
Read through this page to find out what a good answer needs to be like.

Question 4 is worth a whopping 12 marks

1) This question needs a long and <u>detailed</u> answer to get all 12 marks.

2) Remember to use P.E.E. (point, example, explanation).

3) For higher mark questions like this one, the '<u>explanation</u>' part is really important.
   You should make a <u>short point</u> with an <u>example</u>, then write as detailed an
   <u>explanation</u> of how your example backs up your point as you can.

Look for good points like these when you're marking

<u>Show his feelings</u>

- The writer uses words like "apprehensive" to show his feelings. This suggests how
  nervous he was getting as he got closer to his new life at his new school.

- The writer uses alliteration to describe how he went "swooshing" over the sea
  "in a shower of spray". This emphasises the joy he felt in this part of his journey.

- Roald Dahl uses a metaphor when he says "all Headmasters are giants" and when he
  describes how the headmaster gave him a grin that "a shark might give to a small fish".
  This makes the headmaster seem much more dangerous, which adds to Dahl's fear.

<u>Inform the reader</u>

- The writer uses onomatopoeia to describe how he went "swooshing" over the sea.
  This helps the reader to understand the sights and the sounds of Dahl's journey,
  which gives them a better understanding of what is happening.

- He uses straightforward, factual language to inform the reader. For example, he says
  the school is "long" and "three-storeyed" which shows how big it appears to the small
  boy. The words "stone building" show what the school looks like, but also suggest that
  life there will be hard and unpleasant.

Mark question 4 like this

This is the mark scheme for question 4.

Number of marks	What's been written	How it's written	How the answer's put together
Band 1 1-4 marks	A few simple points made without good examples. May only answer one part of the question.	Confusingly written. Might copy out sections of the text.	No clear structure.
Band 2 5-8 marks	Some good points made answering both parts of the question, with some examples to back points up.	More clearly written, often using own words.	Attempt at structure, but not always kept to.
Band 3 9-12 marks	Clear explanation of how language is used to show the author's feelings and tell the reader what is happening. Good examples are used to back points up.	Clearly written in own words, making good use of technical terms.	Well structured, with points linked together making it easy to read.

Sample Answer — Question 4

Time to mark question 4 now.

1) Read the mark scheme and advice on page 40.

2) Use this mark scheme to <u>mark</u> the answer to question 4 below.

3) Then <u>explain</u> why you gave that mark in the lines below the answer.

Now read **Item 3**, *First day* and answer the question below.

4 How does the writer use language to show his feelings and to inform the reader about what is happening?

(12 marks)

Answer

Q4

<u>Show his feelings</u>

Roald Dahl reveals that he was happy during the first part of his journey to school by saying "I liked that part of it". He describes this journey in a positive way, using alliteration like "shower of spray", which emphasises how much fun it was. But then his language changes and becomes more negative. You can tell that he starts to get worried as he uses the word "apprehensive". He tells us that he hadn't ever been away from his family for "a single night", and from this we can tell how worried he was.

The language becomes more descriptive as Dahl uses similes and metaphors to show how he felt about what was happening. He uses a metaphor to describe the headmaster, saying "all Headmasters are giants" and he had a "flashing grin" that a shark might have. These descriptions make it clear that he found him frightening and unpleasant.

<u>Inform the reader</u>

The writer has used clear language to tell us about what was happening. It's written in the first person, "if I remember rightly", so we are told what's going on from Dahl's point of view. He starts off by describing his journey to school, which informs us of what he's doing. The use of onomatopoeia in this description ("swooshing") helps us to imagine the sights and sounds of the journey.

Dahl paints a very clear picture of the school, describing the "three-storeyed stone building" with its "playing-fields" and "football pitches". This is a fairly dull description, but he makes it more interesting and personal by using a simile, "like a private lunatic asylum". He also gives us lots of details, such as the fact that there were "about one hundred and fifty" boys at the school. This makes the extract more informative.

This answer gets ☐ marks out of 12 because ....

....

....

....

....

Mark Scheme — Question 5

Last question now, so it's your last chance to have a go at being the examiner.

For Question 5 you have to compare two items

1) Comparing two items means you need to look for similarities and differences between them.

2) Try and cover both items in the same amount of detail, and don't forget to use P.E.E.

Look for good points like these when you're marking

Titles and subheadings

- The title of Item 2 uses two puns on technical tennis terms, "the tennis ace" and "smashed every record". These puns make the title more entertaining, but also reinforce the idea that the article is about tennis. The title of Item 3, on the other hand, is purely informative. It simply states "First day" which shows that the writer is going to tell us about the start of a new experience in his life.

- Item 2 uses subheadings to divide up the text and tell the reader what each section is about. For example, "Champion for charities" lets us know that he does work for charity. The alliteration here also emphasises that he does a lot of charity work. In contrast to this, Item 3 doesn't use subheadings. This is because it's written in paragraphs like a story, so dividing it up with subheadings would interrupt the flow of the writing.

Pictures / diagrams and captions

- The two photographs in Item 2 illustrate the points the article is making. The first is of Federer holding a trophy which shows that he is successful, the second is of him shaking hands with a boy which shows that he is kind and generous. The photograph in Item 3 also reinforces the text. It shows us what Dahl's school looked like, which links to his description in the text and it also looks quite remote, which links to Dahl's feeling of loneliness.

- The captions under the pictures in Item 2 are informative, they tell us exactly what the pictures show. They are also in italics, which makes it clear that they are not part of the main text. The caption in Item 3 is more entertaining, it just says "the Loony Bin". This links to his description of a "private lunatic asylum" and reveals that Dahl thought it was more of a mad house than a school. It's also written in handwriting, which links it to Dahl's personal opinions.

Mark question 5 like this

This is the mark scheme for question 5.

Number of marks	What's been written	How it's written	How the answer's put together
Band 1 1-4 marks	Not much comparison of the two items, and may not answer both parts of the question.	Confusingly written. Lots of text has been copied.	No clear structure.
Band 2 5-8 marks	Some points made comparing the two items, with an attempt to answer both parts of the question.	More clearly written, mostly using own words.	Attempt at structure (e.g. first talking about the title of one item then comparing it to the other), but not always kept to.
Band 3 9-12 marks	Several clear comparisons made, answering both parts of the question and making use of good examples.	Clearly written making good use of technical terms.	Well structured, with points linked together making it easy to follow.

Sample Answers — Question 5

1) Read the mark scheme on page 42 and use it to <u>mark</u> these answers to question 5.

2) Then <u>explain</u> why you gave those marks in the lines below the answers.

> Now look again at all three items. They have each been presented in a different way.
>
> 5   Choose **two** of these items. Compare them using these headings:
> - the titles and subheadings
> - the pictures / diagrams and captions   *(12 marks)*

Answer 1

Q5

I have chosen Item 2 and Item 3.

<u>Titles and subheadings</u>

     The presentation of the titles is different in the two items. In Item 2 the title is really big and bold to attract the reader's attention and it goes right across the page. In Item 3 the title isn't as big and bold and it is above one of the columns not both of them. It doesn't stand out as much as in Item 2, which means it doesn't grab your attention so much. Item 2 uses subheadings such as "Born to play tennis" which tells you what the paragraph is going to be about. Item 3 doesn't use any subheadings which makes the text flow better.

<u>Pictures / diagrams and captions</u>

     Both items use photos. Item 2 has two photos of Federer, showing him winning a trophy and meeting a little boy. The photos show us what the article is about, his tennis success and his generosity. Item 3 only uses one photo of the school, which is what the text is about. The captions are different too. In Item 2 the captions are typed and in italics but in Item 3 the caption under the photo looks like it is handwritten. This reminds us that the story is being told from Dahl's personal point of view.

This answer gets ☐ marks out of 12 because ....
....
....
....

Answer 2

Q5

<u>Titles and subheadings</u>

     Item 2 is about Federer and how he is really good at tennis and also gives money to charity and Item 3 is about when Roald Dahl went to school and he didn't like it. The titles of the items tell us what they are about.

<u>Pictures / diagrams and captions</u>

     Item 2 has two pictures and Item 3 has one picture so they are different because of that. I like the pictures in Item 2 the best.

This answer gets ☐ marks out of 12 because ....
....
....
....

Practice Exam — Questions

Here are some practice exam questions for 'Understanding non-fiction texts'. They're similar in style to the ones you'll get in <u>Section A</u> of your Unit 1 GCSE English Language or GCSE English exam.

To make it more like the real exam, read all the items and do <u>all the questions</u> in one go and give yourself <u>one hour</u> to do it all. Try to use everything you've learnt so far about what makes a good exam answer...

Read **Item 1**, the article called *Sleeping, please do not disturb!* and answer the questions below.

1   List 4 things the article tells you about how different animals sleep.

(4 marks)

2   What do you learn from the article about why sleep is important?

(4 marks)

Now read **Item 2**, the article called *Sir David Attenborough: Life at the BBC* and answer the question below.

3   What reasons can you find in the article for saying that David Attenborough is interested in wildlife and is a talented broadcaster?

(8 marks)

Now read **Item 3**, *Introducing Argentina* and answer the question below.

4   How does the writer use language to inform you about Argentina and make it sound exciting?

(12 marks)

Now look again at all three items. They have each been presented in interesting but different ways.

5   Choose **two** of these items. Compare how the writers have used presentational devices for effect in the two texts.

(12 marks)

Practice Exam — Item 1

Here's the first text to go with the practice exam questions on page 44. It's an article about sleeping.

Sleeping, please do not disturb!

"Why do I need to sleep, Mum?" You have probably asked your parents this question when you wanted to stay up late. But the answer is simple: sleep is **vital** for our survival. While you are off in the land of Nod, your body is "**recharging**" and your brain is busy organising information and memories. That's why, if we don't get enough sleep, we wake up feeling grumpy and moving clumsily. In fact, it takes only 48 hours without sleep for a person to begin to **hallucinate** — see things that are not really there. Even worse than that, if you don't get regular sleep your **immune system** doesn't work as well, and if you don't sleep at all you'll eventually **die**. The good news is that people who get plenty of sleep every night **live for longer** though.

Animals need their forty winks just like us but they get their ration of sleep in very different ways...

Dozy dolphins

How can you sleep and keep an eye out for enemies at the same time? Dolphins have worked out a clever trick to get some rest without putting themselves at risk. Scientists think that they keep one half of their brain **conscious** while the other goes to sleep. This means that they can sleep-swim up to the surface for air every now and then, and watch out for predators, too.

Catnap

Next time your cat is taking a nap on the sofa, see if he twitches his whiskers or paws — it could mean that he is having a **dream**. Scientists carried out brain scans on sleeping rats and found a pattern of activity in the area of the brain associated with memory, suggesting that the rats were dreaming. They think that dogs and cats could have dreams, too.

Cuddle up

Emperor penguins sleep **standing up**, taking naps of a few minutes at a time. To protect themselves from predators and the icy cold, they stand in groups and take turns to go into the middle, where they can rest in safety. Someone should buy them a duvet.

Hang on

Bats have whopping great wings but their legs and feet are not strong enough to support them standing up or walking around. So at bedtime (which, for nocturnal animals such as bats, is daytime) they take the weight off their tired limbs and just **hang**.

Did you know?

The animal that sleeps the most is the **koala**. These lazy furballs can kip for up to **22 hours** a day!

Practice Exam — Item 2

Here's Item 2. It's an article about the wildlife TV presenter Sir David Attenborough.

Sir David Attenborough: Life at the BBC

JZB / Rex Features

David Attenborough is one of the most widely respected TV broadcasters and has become known as the face and voice of natural history documentaries. His career in broadcasting has stretched over more than a half a century from 1952.

Career at the BBC

After initially being rejected by the BBC, he was later given a three-month training schedule as a broadcaster, and quickly rose through the ranks. He became in charge of all non-fiction broadcasts and was soon associated with various natural history programmes such as *The Pattern of Animals* and *Zoo Quest*. From 1965 to 1969 Attenborough was controller of BBC2. He initiated many programmes including live snooker, *Match of the Day*, *The Likely Lads* and *Mastermind*.

However, David Attenborough is remembered primarily for the natural history series that he wrote and produced. These series used ground-breaking filming techniques and his ease of presentation made the material very accessible and of interest to a new generation of viewers.

His major series included:
- *Life on Earth* (1979)
- *The Living Planet* (1984)
- *The Trials of Life* (1990)
- *Life in the Freezer* (1993)
- *The Private Life of Plants* (1995)
- *The Life of Birds* (1998)
- *The Life of Mammals* (2002)
- *Life in the Undergrowth* (2005)
- *Planet Earth* (2006)
- *Life In Cold Blood* (2008)

The key to David's appeal is his ability to share his genuine enthusiasm and love for wildlife — wildlife broadcasting will be forever associated with his distinctive and calming voice. A survey found that David Attenborough was the most trusted of British celebrities.

David Attenborough and Environmental Issues

In recent years David has become much more outspoken on issues such as environmental damage, global warming and extinction of particular species. He has stated that human overpopulation and global warming (caused by human activity) are the *root cause* of much of the world's growing environmental problems. He has lent his voice to organisations such as WWF®* in their fight to protect certain species and campaign for wildlife.

*WWF® — the World Wide Fund for Nature

Practice Exam — Item 3

This is the third text you'll need for the exam questions on page 44. It's a page from a travel website.

Introducing Argentina

The secret is out: with its gorgeous landscapes, exciting cities and lively culture, Argentina is a traveller's paradise. It stretches almost 3500km from Bolivia to the tip of South America, has a wide range of geography and climates, and is almost the size of India.

Some of Argentina's most dramatic mountains

Fast Facts about Argentina
- Area: 2.8 million sq km
- Languages: mainly Spanish
- Population: 40, 301, 927
- Capital: Buenos Aires

Something for everyone
Nature-lovers can traverse the Patagonian steppe, climb South America's highest peak, walk among thousands of penguins and witness the world's most amazing waterfalls. Hikers can sample the stunning scenery of the lush Lake District — with its glorious lakes and white-tipped mountains — and revel in Patagonia's glacier-carved landscapes and painted Andean deserts. City slickers will adore fabulous Buenos Aires, full of opportunities to learn Spanish, watch fútbol (soccer), dance the sexy tango and interact with dynamic and beautiful porteños (Buenos Aires locals). You'll be out shopping for designer clothes at affordable prices and eating the world's best steaks every day while partying at nightclubs all night long.

It's party time
Argentina celebrated a big anniversary in 2010, rejoicing in 200 years of independence from Spain. Expect to visit several recently renovated museums and buildings, such as the famous Teatro Colón which shut down popular tours for over two years during its facelift.

What are you waiting for?
Argentina is safe, friendly and — compared to Europe or the US — very affordable. Now is a great time to visit, so get your spirit in gear and prepare for an unforgettable adventure!

Our Top Picks For Argentina
1. Iguazú Falls: witness the mighty roar of South America's greatest spectacle.
2. Buenos Aires: experience porteño passions: tango, soccer, food, fashion and fantastically frenzied nightlife.
3. Glacier Perito Moreno: see (and hear!) this mighty river of ice.

Acknowledgements

The Publisher would like to thank the following copyright holders for permission to reproduce texts and images:

Webpage on page 31 entitled 'Climate change explained'. Reproduced with kind permission from the Environment Agency.

Page 32: Photographs © JHA / Juergen Hasenkopf / Rex Features

With thanks to David Higham Associates Ltd for permission to use the extract on page 33 entitled 'First day' from *Boy* by Roald Dahl. Published by Jonathan Cape Ltd & Penguin Books Ltd.

Article on page 45 entitled 'Sleeping, please do not disturb!' © The Times 2010 / nisyndication.com

With thanks to Tejvan Pettinger for permission to use the David Attenborough article/biography on page 46. www.biographyonline.net

Page 46: Photograph © JZB / Rex Features

Article on page 47 entitled 'Introducing Argentina'. Reproduced with permission from the Lonely Planet website www.lonelyplanet.com © 2010 Lonely Planet.

Every effort has been made to locate copyright holders and obtain permission to reproduce texts and images. For those texts and images where it has been difficult to trace the originator of the work, we would be grateful for information. If any copyright holder would like us to make an amendment to the acknowledgements, please notify us and we will gladly update the book at the next reprint. Thank you.